MY BAPTISM

A Learning, Coloring & Activity Booklet

Beth Whittaker

Covenant Communications Inc.
American Fork, Utah

Printed in the United States of America   First Printing: February 2015

ISBN 978-1-62108-970-4

YOUR 8ᵀᴴ BIRTHDAY IS SPECIAL!

Now you are old enough to be accountable for your actions. This means that you know right from wrong, and you can choose to be baptized!

Can you find eight number 8s on this page?

4ᵗʰ Article of Faith

"We believe that the first principles and ordinances of the Gospel are: first, Faith in the Lord Jesus Christ; second, Repentance; third, Baptism by immersion for the remission of sins; fourth, Laying on of hands for the gift of the Holy Ghost."

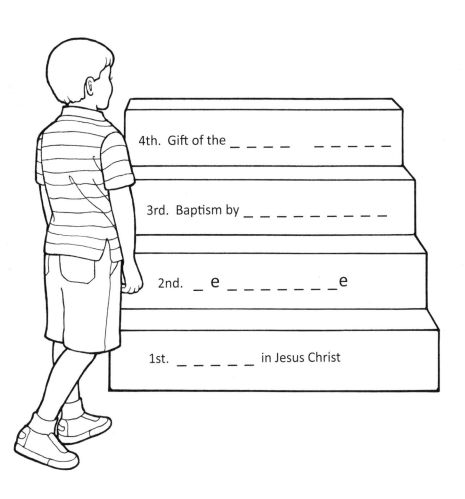

4th. Gift of the _ _ _ _   _ _ _ _ _ _

3rd. Baptism by _ _ _ _ _ _ _ _ _ _

2nd. _ e _ _ _ _ _ _ _ _e

1st. _ _ _ _ _ in Jesus Christ

Learning about the *principles* of faith and repentance will help you to prepare for the *ordinances* of baptism and confirmation.

Fill in the missing words above.

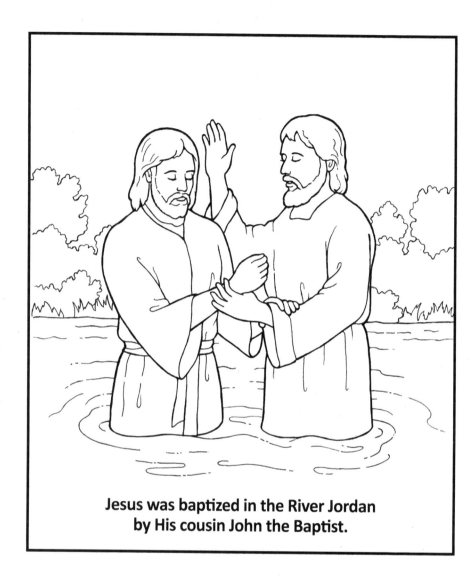

**Jesus was baptized in the River Jordan
by His cousin John the Baptist.**

When Jesus was on the earth, He was baptized to teach us by His example to keep all of God's commandments. He was baptized by immersion. This means He was completely covered by water.

Jesus taught us that the covenants we make when we are baptized are very important.

A covenant is a two-way promise we make with our Heavenly Father. We make promises to Him, and He promises blessings to us in return.

We promise to

- Obey His commandments
- Forgive others
- Remember Jesus and follow His example

Heavenly Father promises to

- Forgive us when we repent
- Give us the gift of the Holy Ghost
- Let us live with Him forever

Fill in each of the shapes that have dots to find a hidden word.

Every Sunday when you listen to the sacrament prayer you will be reminded of the covenants you made at baptism.

If you have done something wrong, you can repent and ask Heavenly Father for forgiveness. Then, as you take the bread and water and have faith in Jesus Christ, your sins will be washed away—just as they were on your baptism day!

When we sincerely repent and then take the sacrament, we can feel as clean as we did on our baptism day . . . like a beautiful spring day after the rain.

Baptism is the first ordinance we receive on the covenant path back to our Heavenly Father.

Start

Nephi said:

"The gate by which ye should enter is repentance and baptism by water . . ."

(2 Nephi 31:17)

*Follow the maze.

After you are baptized, you will be confirmed a member of The Church of Jesus Christ of Latter-day Saints by a worthy priesthood holder who has been given power from God.

You will also receive a very special gift—the gift of the Holy Ghost.

As you try to make good choices and follow Jesus, the Holy Ghost will always be with you.

The Holy Ghost is sometimes called "the Comforter." Whenever you are sad or worried or afraid, you can pray to Heavenly Father, and He will send you comfort through the Holy Ghost. This might feel like a warm blanket being wrapped around you.

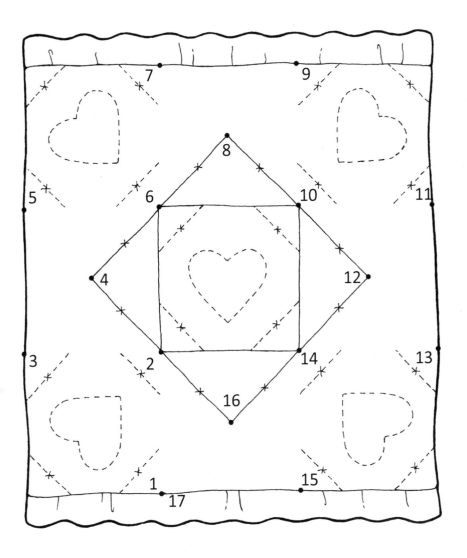

Connect the dots to finish the pattern on the quilt, and then color it!

The Holy Ghost

- Helps you to know what things are true
- Can guide you and warn you of danger
- Comforts you when you are sad or afraid
- Gives you a warm, happy feeling in your heart when you choose the right

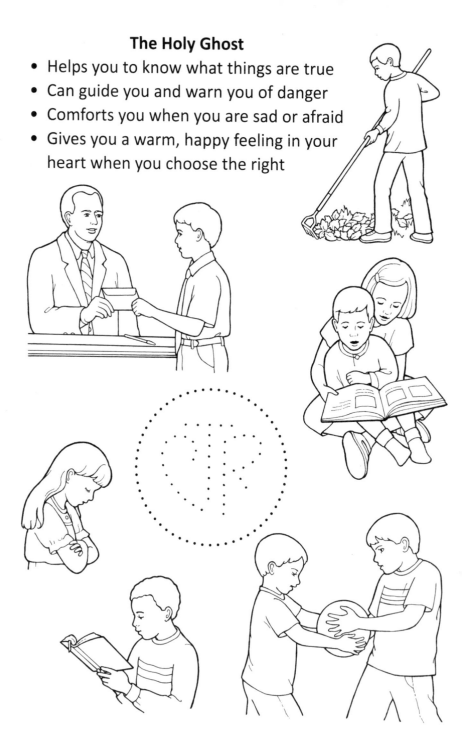

*Connect the dots to make the CTR shield in the center, and then draw a line to the CTR from each of the children who are choosing the right.

Baptism Word Search

s	e	p	r	v	d	h	r	m	x	b	t	y
s	i	h	v	i	m	m	e	r	s	i	o	n
p	g	c	a	u	n	g	n	q	a	j	h	v
y	h	d	o	b	a	p	t	i	s	m	h	f
a	t	p	t	m	p	t	c	z	r	y	s	o
n	b	o	r	a	f	e	n	l	s	x	k	r
w	h	i	t	e	n	o	l	m	e	g	z	g
f	o	h	w	o	p	w	r	i	k	a	o	i
c	o	n	f	i	r	m	a	t	i	o	n	v
x	f	y	q	g	o	w	a	t	e	r	n	e
w	a	h	k	x	m	k	n	f	p	r	a	v
b	i	m	a	j	i	t	e	m	p	l	e	p
g	t	w	e	f	s	n	r	g	i	f	t	k
s	h	z	p	y	e	r	j	z	r	s	o	m

eight
comforter
temple
confirmation
faith

promise
white
forgive
baptism
gift

immersion
water
clean

What things can help you keep your baptismal covenants?
There are two ideas in the pictures below.

Find the differences in both sets of pictures above. Circle 6 things that are different in each picture on the right side.

When you make and keep your baptismal covenants, you are on the path that leads to the temple and someday back to your Heavenly Father.

I was baptized on

I was baptized by

The witnesses were

I was confirmed by

When I was baptized and confirmed I felt

*Draw yourself being baptized.